Little Blue Book
Stories #10-17

Written by Amy Fullmer and Joan Parrish   •   **Illustrated by Barclay Tucker and Kedrick Ridges**

Discover Intensive Phonics for Yourself ®
Reading Horizons

Contents

#10

The Box

Manual Lesson 34
Computer Lesson 41

Once I was passing a box that was dripping.

I could see many slobs that were gulping
and sipping.

They were messing the box. It was
sloppy and wet. They were all cramming in,
the slobs and the pets.

The fox and the frog, the hen and
the ox, were kidding and calling, they just
would not stop!

They kept asking their friends to come in for the fun, but if they kept cramming the fun would be done.

I yelled to the slobs, "It's too crammed
up there. You all must stop hopping, your
box, it will tear!"

They kept on filling. Those slobs
would not stop all the cramming, the
gulping, and spilling.

The box was all wet now, the box was
stuffed. And then came the ripping, it was
going to bust!

I ran from the box with its slobs and its dripping.

Then came more ripping and the slobs, they were flipping.

This way and that, slipping and sliding they went.

Not one slob was left where their fun had been spent.

I went back to the spot where the box had once been. There was no dripping, no spilling, no box, and no hen.

Comprehension Questions

1. What was wrong with the box?

2. What was being crammed in the box?

3. Who was making the box a mess?

4. What happened to the box?

5. What happened to the slobs?

MCWs

been   they
done   who
friend   would
one
once
see
their
there

Skill Words

asking   passing
being   pets
calling   ripping
crammed   sipping
cramming   sliding
dripping   slipping
filling   slobs
flipping   spilling
going   stuffed
gulping   yelled
hopping
kidding
messing

Words beyond skill level

back   more   then   with
happen   sloppy   those   wrong
many   tear   way

13

Me
A Poem

Manual Lesson 36
Computer Lesson 43

Me and I stand,
We walk hand in hand,
Having fun as we go
It should be so.
Being with me is grand.

MCWs

and
as
in
is
it
should
walk

Skill Words

be
go
me
so
we

Words beyond skill level

with

The Raft

Manual Lesson 36

Fred is a frog.

He lives on a pad on the pond.

He has a small raft.

Fred is on his raft drifting on the pond.

He naps on his raft in the hot sun.

Fog drifts onto the pond.

Fred stands up on the raft.

He cannot see his pad.

Fred is getting sad!

"I cannot see my pad! I cannot get off the raft! What am I to do?"

"I am here to help you, my friend!" said Jo.

Jo is Fred's best friend and he lives at the pond, too.

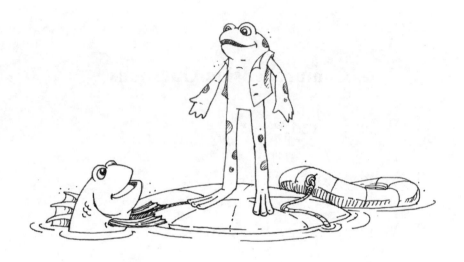

Jo put a string on the raft and pulled Fred to his pad.

"You are the best friend! You helped me!" said Fred.

"I'm so glad. Let's go and have some big bugs," said Jo.

Comprehension Questions

1. What is Fred?

2. Where does he live?

3. What does Fred like to do?

4. Why was Fred sad?

5. Who helped Fred to his pad?

6. Who are friends? Why?

MCWs

are	off	too
do	pull	you
does	put	
friend	said	
has	see	
in	some	
is	the	
my	to	

Skill Words

big	sad
bug	so
drift	string
Fred	sun
get	
help	
hot	
Jo	
nap	
pad	
pond	
pulled	
raft	

Words beyond skill level

cannot	live
help	onto
like	

27

#13

Silent E!

Manual Lesson 37
Computer Lesson 44

If there is one thing I could be, I'd want to be a silent E.

There's tons of words he can make new.
I'll tell you now, there's not a few.

He can work a lot of fun. Add an E,
that's how it's done.

If you're at home, it's time you ate.
Take off your cap, put on a cape.

Snag a fin and call it fine.

Take a spin, don't twist your spine.

Silent E can make a plan into a new jet plane.

He can fix your brother Sam...

he will not be the same.

We now have glade, we did have glad. I
hope we have not made you mad.

You want a twin, he'll give you twine.
He'll make dim a shining dime!

I must quit now. It's lat, no late.

Silent E is quite a mate!

Comprehension Questions

1. What does the boy want to be?

2. What does Silent E want to do?

3. What can you put on?

4. How can plan be a new jet plane?

5. Why is it time to quit?

MCWs

brother	want
does	word
done	work
don't	
on	
off	
put	
there	

Skill Words

ate	quite
cape	same
dime	spine
fine	take
glade	time
give	twine
home	
hope	
late	
made	
make	
mate	
plane	

Words beyond skill level

boy	into	silent
few	new	thing
how	now	why

#14

The Prince
and the Mule
(A chapter story)

Manual Lesson 39
Computer Lesson 46

Once there was a kind Prince. He lived
with his father, the King. The Prince had
a pet mule named Sal. The Prince liked to
ride her.

The King did not like his son riding a mule. He felt strange in front of his friends. So, the King gave the Prince a prancing mare. The Prince was grateful for the mare but he still rode Sal, his mule.

The King was mad that his son would not ride the prancing mare. He went to the Prince and said, "Son, you like your mule, Sal, a lot, but she is a pet. You will not find a wife riding a mule! No dame will glance at you twice. No mule will win a race and your cape drags in the dust!"

The Prince was kind to his father, but he would not change his mind. "Father," he said, "Sal is my pet and my friend. I like riding her."

The King had to change his son's mind. He came up with a plan to trap the Prince. The King used his son's kindness to trap him, for the Prince was kind to all.

II. The Trap

The King called his son and asked him to go to the baker's to get a cake. The Prince sent for his mule and rode off. As the Prince and Sal went to the baker's, they came upon a man. The man walked in front of Sal and the Prince could tell the man was ill. The Prince jumped off his mule. "Can I help you get home?" he asked the man. "I can take you there on my mule."

The Prince did take the man home.
When they got there, the man said, "Thank
you, thank you! I was feeling so ill. My
wife and I are of an old age and we have no
mule."

The Prince felt sad. "I would like to
give you my mule so you and your wife will
have one to use," he said.

The Prince walked home. He missed Sal.

When he got home, the King met him.
"Where is the cake?" he asked.

The Prince told his father of the old man
and the mule.

The King acted sad that Sal was gone but
he would not miss the mule.

III. Glad to Sad

The King wasted no time. He sent for the prancing marc. "Let's take a ride," he said to the Prince. "We can have a grand race."

The King's eyes were full of pride as he raced with his son. His son was a gent upon the prancing mare. The Prince's cape waved in the wind as the mare went gliding on.

The King felt glad. Life was grand.

Just then, the Prince had his mare stop. They were in front of a small home. The Prince jumped off his mare and went up to an old man. The Prince and the man talked. Then, with a smile, the man left.

"Where did he go?" the King asked.

"We are making a trade," said the
Prince.

When the old man came, the King was
sad. "Oh, no!" he said. The old man had the
Prince's mule. The Prince was giving the
old man his prancing mare in trade for the
mule.

The King's trap did not work, and the Prince rode off on Sal, his cape dragging in the dust.

Comprehension Questions

1. What kind of pet did the Prince have?

2. Why did the King give the Prince a prancing mare?

3. Give two reasons why the King didn't like the mule.

4. What did the King send the Prince to get?

5. What was wrong with the old man?

6. Why did the King feel glad?

7. Why didn't the King's trap work?

MCWs

are	on	would
asked	once	
eye	she	
friend	that	
full	there	
give	they	
of	were	
off	work	

Skill Words

age	wife
change	
dame	
gent	
glance	
jumped	
king	
mule	
prance	
prince	
race	
trade	
twice	

Words beyond skill level

feel	kind	talk	two	why
feeling	kindness	thank	upon	with
grateful	old	then	walk	wrong

60

15

The Trail of Slime

Manual Lesson 40
Computer Lesson 47

As I walked in the trees, near my feet I could see a small trail of slime. Where was it going? What could it be?

I had to find out what had made this slime trail, and where was it going? Did it have a tail? I could walk near the trail and get to the end and there I would find it -- be it foe -- be it friend.

So I walked and I walked and I
dreamed of a beast spitting out slime. He'd
have me for his feast.

It could be a frog. They're quite small
you see, croaking and hopping, leaving
slime at their feet.

It could be a leak from an eel. Do they leak? No! That's not it. Eels live in the sea.

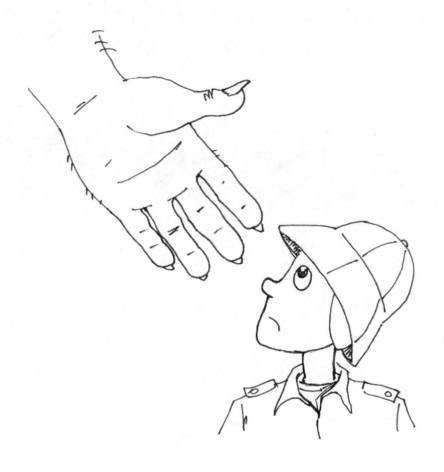

It could be a giant I'm going to seek.
Walking heel to toe -- him I'd not like to
meet.

Then I could see that trail of slime stopped near a great big oak tree. Was it up in the top?

A snap of a twig made me pull up with fear. It could be mean and big and near. I was going to scream. I was going to wail. I needed to get off this trail.

That's when it climbed up the trunk of
the tree -- the one who had made the slime
trail that led me.

It was too small to scare, not a giant or beast. I had no need to fear, no, not in the least.

For there, at the end of the long slime trail, on the giant oak tree, was a small, green snail.

Comprehension Questions

1. What did she see near her feet?

2. Where is the girl walking?

3. What did she dream?

4. Where did the slime stop?

5. What was "The Slime"?

MCWs

could	there
friend	they
off	too
one	was
pull	who
see	
that	
their	

Skill Words

beast	mean	toe
croak	meet	wail
dream	near	
eel	need	
feast	oak	
fear	sea	
feet	see	
foe	seek	
green	scream	
heel	snail	
leak	tail	
least	trail	
leave	tree	

Words beyond skill level

girl	out	when
giant	then	with
great	walk	

#16

I Shouldn't

Manual Lesson 42
Computer Lesson 49

I couldn't, I shouldn't, I wouldn't, I won't. And if you think that it's pink that I like...well I don't.

You aren't making me eat it, you can't, you're too small. I'm faster and bigger, I'd run and you'd fall.

Haven't you heard me? Don't you see?
It just isn't mine, it's theirs, ask them, you'll
see.

Now you look at me, we're not going to eat this, we shouldn't, it isn't my treat. Let's go find out who has put this here. It could be that they've left it. They haven't I fear.

We're not meaning to bug you but, that treat, is it yours? We would like a bite, if you'd let us of course.

He's sure it's not theirs. There's no one
else here! That means it's mine, I'll have
some now.

I'm glad we can eat it, I'm glad that it's mine, but oh we've let it sit out for quite a long time.

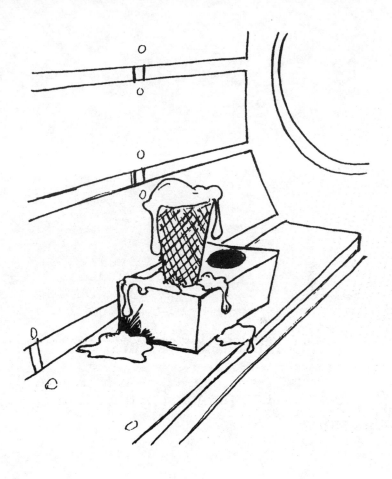

I am so sad, what a deal we've been
dealt. I said we couldn't, I said that I
wouldn't, but we could have, we should
have, for we just let it melt.

Comprehension Questions

There are no comprehension questions for this story.

MCWs

ask	should
been	that
don't	their
go	too
of	we
one	who
put	won't
see	would

Skill Words

aren't	there's
can't	they've
couldn't	we're
don't	we've
haven't	won't
he's	wouldn't
I'd	you'd
I'll	you'll
I'm	you're
isn't	
it's	
let's	
shouldn't	

Words beyond skill level

course	out	think
look	sure	this
now	them	

17

Hot Dog

Manual Lesson 43
Computer Lesson 50

Ben was busy digging a hole in the grass when he spied them: a pile of hot dogs so big they must have weighed a ton! There was enough meat to feed men, women, lots of kids and...a dog!

The hot dogs were for a wedding. The son of Ben's "man" would soon marry. All of his friends were coming to eat and give gifts.

"I'll have to work fast or the hot dogs will be gone," said Ben. He could see that all the men and women were busy. If he wanted a hot dog--and he did--he'd have to snag it now and bury it. Ben made sure all the men fixing the meal were busy. He crept past them, grabbed a hot dog and ran.

After he was out of sight, he peeked.
No one had seen him. He had made it! "That
was fun!" said Ben. "Now to bury it!" Ben
made a hole, buried the hot dog, then laid in
the grass to rest. He could just taste the hot
dog now. Yummm! Should he get more than
one?

He guessed that many friends would be
coming to see the boy marry, but there were
enough hot dogs! He would go once more
and carry as many as he could hold!

"I might get as many as eight," Ben
said. The men were still busy. He crept to
the door. Before any of the men could see,
Ben dashed in, grabbed five hot dogs, and
ran! He could tell he'd been fast.

But what was that yelling?
"The dog!"
He'd been seen! The bride's mother
was coming out of the home. "Get that dog,"
she yelled. Ben wasn't quite sure what to do.
He could not out run the woman with five
hot dogs in his lips.

Well, if he couldn't out run her, he
might as well give up the hot dogs. He
didn't want to be put in his pen for sneaking
the meat. Ben had made up his mind. He
went to the door, dropped the hot dogs in a
pile, and ran to the place he hid before.

From his hiding place, he could see the men and the bride's mother all standing by the pile. The hot dogs did have a bit of grass on them and a lot of spit, but he could tell, without seeing their faces, that they were glad he had given them back.

Comprehension Questions

1. What was Ben the dog doing?

2. Why were there hot dogs?

3. What did Ben do with the hot dogs he stole?

4. How many hot dogs did Ben go back and get?

5. What was on the hot dogs that would make you not want to eat them?

MCWs

any	eight	weigh
been	enough	woman
before	give	women
bury	guess	work
busy	marry	
by	many	
carry	sure	
door	that	

Skill Words

crept	laid
eat	meal
feed	meat
five	men
gift	might
give	mind
glad	place
gone	pile
grabbed	sight
hole	sneaking
hot	snag
I'll	taste
kid	yelling

Words beyond skill level

after	given	out	sure	when
back	her	soon	than	with
by	now	spied	them	without